NEWTS
of the British Isles

PATRICK J. WISNIEWSKI

CONTENTS

Cover: *Male smooth newt in full breeding dress.*

Series editor: Jim Flegg.

Copyright © 1989 by P. J. Wisniewski. First published 1989.
Number 47 in the Shire Natural History series. ISBN 0 7478 0029 4.

Printed in Great Britain by C. I. Thomas & Sons (Haverfordwest) Ltd, Press Buildings, Merlins Bridge, Haverfordwest, Dyfed.

Introduction

Newts belong to a class of vertebrates (animals with backbones) called the Amphibia. Amphibians appeared in the fossil record during the Devonian period (about 350 million years ago) and became the dominant terrestrial animals during the Carboniferous period (between 345 and 280 million years ago). These early amphibians were often massive creatures with body scales though, like modern species, they probably spent their juvenile stages as tadpoles. The word 'amphibian' derives from the Greek and means 'double-life', a reference to their ability to live in water and on land. Modern amphibians mostly lack scales and have skin glands which keep the body moist to allow for respiration (breathing) through the skin. Amphibians are cold-blooded or ectothermic: they cannot regulate their body temperature as mammals do except by moving themselves to areas of warmth or cold.

Amphibians are found throughout tropical and temperate parts of the world but, unlike many animal groups, are unable to cross salt-water barriers and so are severely hampered in their ability to colonise islands actively.

Today three amphibian orders remain: the Apoda or caecilians, a primitive group which live in tropical forest areas where they burrow through damp earth and closely resemble earthworms in external appearance; the Anura or frogs and toads; and the Urodela, the tailed amphibians or newts and salamanders.

The study of amphibians and reptiles is herpetology, derived from the Greek word *herpeton*, meaning a crawling thing, a remarkable misnomer considering how many amphibians, including urodeles, can run, jump, climb and, in the case of some frogs, even glide.

There are 3000 to 4000 amphibian species the majority of which are frogs and toads. Urodeles form the next largest group with over 300 species, found mainly in the northern temperate regions and to a lesser extent the tropics. Most urodeles are terrestrial but usually need to return to water for reproduction, even in those species where courtship occurs on land. A courtship display is generally part of the pattern of breeding behaviour.

Although British newts have the scientific name *Triturus*, the name 'newt' has no scientific definition. Smaller urodeles which spend a lot of time in water tend to be called newts, whilst larger more terrestrial species are called salamanders. The word 'newt' has an interesting origin, starting life as the Anglo-Saxon *evete* (or *efete*) from which we get the other name in modern usage 'eft'. 'Eft' mutated to 'ewt' which because of difficulties in the pronunciation of 'an ewt' became 'a newt'. Newts have also been called 'undines', after the female water sprite of European mythology and 'triton' after the Greek man-fish god. To confuse matters, in bygone times the name 'newt' was also used for lizards with which the newts were classified until 1880. To this day the common lizard is occasionally referred to as a 'furze evet', an echo of this misclassification.

In Lancashire both lizards and newts are called 'askers', in Scotland *dearc luachrach* (berry among the rushes) and in Wales *geneugoeg* (false mouth) or 'madfall'. The newt has never figured to any extent in myths and folklore unlike its larger cousin the European fire salamander (*Salamandra salamandra*). According to legend this innocuous creature lived in and drew energy from fire and could be used to douse an inferno or protect against lightning. Asbestos was thought to be wool grown by the salamander! At the same time, the salamander was considered so poisonous that it could kill whole tribes or render lethal the fruit of trees under which it sat. Its vomit was thought to cause blindness and it was believed that when a salamander bit it would never let go. Despite this the animal featured in the crest of one of the French royal families. In Ireland a similar fearful reputation was bestowed upon the newt, where it was called 'dark-looker' or 'man-eater' and was said to enter the mouth of a sleeper and invade the body.

Shakespeare knew the newt, mentioning it in King Lear and including 'eye of newt' in the witches' potion in *Macbeth*. Otherwise there is little evidence that newts were included in spells or potions during magic ritual.

One curious bit of urodele trivia concerns the discovery of a large fossil salamander which in 1725 was claimed to be the skeleton of the man who witnessed the Deluge and was thus cited as proof of the Bible story!

The British newts

Pleistocene fossil remains from Kent indicate that the palmate newt was present in Britain some 10,000 years ago. Presently three species are widely distributed on mainland Britain but only the smooth newt occurs in Ireland. Ireland separated from mainland Britain whilst the latter was still joined to continental Europe by a land bridge, thus allowing little time for colonisation. Presumably the cold-tolerant smooth newt was able to follow the retreating glaciers more closely than the other species.

The smooth newt has the widest British distribution though it is less common in Scotland and Wales (where, like all newts, it is under-recorded), scattered in Ireland and present on Guernsey. The palmate is common in western Britain and is found on the Scillies and Jersey. The crested is most common in southern and eastern England but occurs in a few places in Scotland and is uncommon in Wales.

All three species of newt are native to the British Isles. All are also found in continental Europe. The common, smooth or spotted newt (*Triturus vulgaris*) is the most widely distributed, occurring in nine or more sub-species east to the Yenisey River, USSR, north to Sweden and Finland and south to Greece and western Turkey. It is absent from southern France, the Iberian Peninsula, Corsica and Sardinia. The great crested, warty or great water newt (*T. cristatus*), likewise has a wide distribution extending eastwards to just beyond the Urals whilst three very similar species occur in southern Europe. The palmate newt (*T. helveticus*) which was not recognised in Britain until 1843, has a distinctly western range: occurring in France, northern Spain and Portugal (where there is a dwarf sub-species), Belgium, the Netherlands, western Germany, Switzerland and north-west Italy.

Several species have been introduced to Britain. Alpine crested newts (*T. carnifex*) are successfully established whilst marbled newts (*T. marmoratus*) and ribbed newts (*Pleurodeles waltl*) have survived in garden ponds. Fire salamanders are recorded as escapes and the cave salamander (*Hydromantes genei*) was introduced though probably no longer persists. Most successful has been the alpine newt (*T. alpestris*) with colonies in Shropshire, Berkshire, Sussex and elsewhere. It lives well in garden ponds though prefers larger pools and can establish itself from small founder colonies and without competing with native species.

Distinguishing native British species is fairly easy though females and juveniles can be problematical. The differences are summarised in tables 1 and 2. Crested newts are the largest and most slender species and large thickset specimens are usually females though, on average, males and females are of similar size. Stunted populations do occur, this being true of all the native species. In the smaller smooth newt males tend to be longer than females, which are heavier and slightly rougher-skinned. The palmate is the smallest native amphibian though it is the males which are small since females are, on average, similar in size to female smooths. The male palmate has a proportionally shorter tail than the male smooth.

During breeding the newt's colours become lighter and more intense. Outside the breeding season, the crests and foot fringes are almost absent whilst the laterally flattened tail becomes more rounded. Non-breeding female palmates may develop a yellowish or reddish stripe down the middle of the back. The body of the smooth newt becomes less rounded when not breeding while the palmate becomes angular during the breeding season due to the swelling of ridges of muscle and skin along the length of the back.

Female smooths and palmates are best

distinguished by looking for the generally unspotted throat of the latter and the more delicate belly pattern, obvious dorsal stripes and smaller feet.

It is not unknown for newts to change sex, although this has not yet been reported in Britain. However, starved male alpine newts have been seen to turn into females!

The larvae are more difficult to iden-

Table 1. Distinguishing features of adult newts

General	Crested	Smooth	Palmate
Size	11-16 cm, exceptionally 20 cm	8-11 cm	7-11 cm
Skin	Rough; on land always appears moist	Smooth; on land velvety	As smooth
Legs	Long and dainty ringed with brown and yellow bands	Unringed	Unringed
Throat colour	Dirty white with brown marbling	White with dark spots or speckles	White or pinkish with no speckling
Tail size	Less than half total body length	Half total body length	Usually less than half total body length
Breeding Male			
Dorsal colour	Grey to black, with round dark spots on head, body and tail; iridescent white spots on flanks	Brown to olive, with darker spots	Olive-brown, spotted and marbled with darker colours which may fuse to form two lines along the back
Belly colour	Yellow to vermilion, with grey to black spots or vermiculations	Yellow to red, spotted with black	Outer edge whitish, central area straw-yellow to orange with fine speckling
Tail colour	Silver to blue stripe along side; underside yellow to vermilion	Lower edge orange; cloaca and tip black; sides bluish	Lower edge yellowish; cloaca dark; two rows of dark spots present with yellow to light brown between. Black filament extends 5 mm from tip
Crest	Spiky on dorsal surface, smooth on underside of tail, interrupted at base of tail	Wavy, uninterrupted to 1 cm high; tipped with black	Low, smooth and uninterrupted ending abruptly at tail tip
Head	No longitudinal grooves. Dark	Three longitudinal grooves and five stripes, one passing through the eye	Rounded with three longitudinal grooves; a dark stripe runs along the side of the head passing through the eye
Feet	No webs or foot fringes	Broad fringes on hind toes	Dark; webs between hind toes
Body shape	Round in cross-section	As crested	Box-like in cross-section

(continued)

4

1. *The alpine newt has successfully established itself in several parts of the British Isles.*

2. *Aquatic female smooth newt. Female smooths are very difficult to distinguish from female palmates.*

Breeding female

Dorsal colour	As male, though often darker	Yellowish to olive-brown, with dark freckling and often two parallel lines down back on to tail	Similar to smooth, but parallel lines more frequent
Crest	Shallow, dorsal groove only. Narrow, smooth tail crest	No dorsal crest though dorsal ridge often present; tail crest well developed and smooth	As smooth
Head	Dark	Single dark line through eye	As smooth
Feet	Large with long toes	Proportionally larger than palmate	Proportionally smaller than smooth

tify, particularly the more cylindrical ones of the smooth and palmate. It is said that these two may be distinguished by comparing the distance between the nostril and nearest eye with the eye diameter: in the smooth newtlet this is similar whilst in the palmate the diameter exceeds the nostril-eye distance. In practice this is impossible to determine and it is better to wait until the newtlets are ready to metamorphose, when the palmates develop pink or brown bellies and the smooth newts orange ones.

Some mention should be made of the freaks which occasionally turn up in populations. Limbs, in particular, are prone to abnormalities, possibly because they are more susceptible to physical damage and then regrow in an eccentric fashion, though agricultural chemicals have also been shown to induce limb deformities in frog tadpoles.

At one pond, 4 per cent of newts exhibited supernumerary or bifurcated toes and a further 4 per cent had atrophied or reduced numbers of toes. These abnormalities mainly occurred on the hind feet and both males and females

Table 2. Distinguishing features of newt eggs and larvae

Egg	Crested	Smooth/palmate
Colour	Yellowish-white	Brownish or greyish-brown
Size	4.5 mm	3 mm
Larva		
Hatching size	8 mm	6 mm
Maximum size	5-8 cm	4 cm
Tail	Long and tapering with filament	No filament
Colour	Brown with dark spots on body and tail	Light clay with fine speckling; occasionally yellow spots on back
Head	No bar through eye	Well grown larva often has a bar through the eye
Habits	Often swims in mid-water	Rarely swims in mid-water; stays on the bottom

were affected. Truncated tails, missing and even additional limbs and tails have been recorded and full webbing has been observed on the hind feet of some male smooth newts. Most curious of all is the report of a double-headed hybrid tadpole between a smooth and palmate newt.

Albinism occurs in smooth and crested newts and melanism (when the animal appears totally black) in the latter.

Where newts live

Newts have preferred habitats though they do occasionally occur in extraordinary places, like the group of crested newts removed from a coal bunker in South Wales.

The smooth newt, being the commonest British species, is found in the widest range of habitats: upland, lowland, woodland, plantation, heathland, marsh, farmland and urban. It breeds in all types of standing water as well as brooks. It will lay eggs in very small pools and hence it is the species which usually colonises garden ponds unless these are very exposed or heavily shaded. Smooth newt ponds tend to be shallow, up to one metre deep and often of a temporary nature. They are usually weedy, providing protection for newtlets. Smooth newts tolerate a wide pH range (a measure of acidity and alkalinity where pH 7 is neutral) and high concentrations of metallic ions, especially calcium. In Epping Forest they are found in pools on clay, avoiding those on more acidic or gravel soils, and in the Peak District they are found in alkaline pools on limestone to an altitude of 380 metres. Yet in Sweden they breed in acidic forest ponds of pH 4 to 5 and in acidified lakes where their populations have increased as acid rain has destroyed fish stocks. Ponds with large numbers of fish do not usually support large smooth newt populations for obvious reasons. The presence of frogs in a pond may be beneficial as newts are known to eat tadpoles.

The palmate is also a newt of small ponds, its requirements differing somewhat from those of the smooth newt

3. *Newt ponds usually have an abundance of aquatic and marginal vegetation. This man-made pond supports breeding smooth newts and was photographed just prior to the breeding season.*

4. *Two male great crested newts showing the typical colours and jagged crest present during the breeding season as well as the characteristically warty skin.*

5. *Female crested newt during the breeding season.*

6. *Male (right) and female palmates, the smallest British newts. Note the dark, webbed hind feet of the male and the filament on the end of the tail.*

7. *An albino crested newt. Partial albinos also occur and have a harlequin appearance.*

though in some localities the species do occur together (sometimes also with the crested and, on the continent of Europe, the alpine newt). It also frequents slow running water and lakes and has been known to breed in bomb craters and brackish water. It usually avoids fish ponds but on Rhum it frequents lochs alongside brown trout, where the newts avoid the fish by remaining in the shallows. The palmate inhabits deciduous forest, heath, orchards, gardens, farmland, wet grassland and marshes, and prefers clearer less eutrophic (nutrient rich) pools than the smooth newt and is also less successful at colonising garden ponds.

Palmate newt ponds tend to be acidic and it is for this reason that the species is so often incorrectly referred to as 'montane', as many upland pools are acidic. However, palmates may be found in lowland areas and in Sussex are commoner at lower altitude, whilst in the Peak District smooth and crested are to be found at greater altitude than the palmate. Nevertheless, in Scotland palmates are found at altitudes of over 880 metres and in the Pyrenees at 2000 metres. Curiously, despite the fact that palmates prefer acidic pools down to pH 3.9, they have been observed breeding in alkaline pools to pH 9.5 in continental Europe. Perhaps some other factor such as water hardness (they seem to prefer soft water though they do on occasion use hardwater chalk ponds) or tolerance of low concentrations of metallic ions, especially potassium, may affect their choice of breeding pond.

Palmates are probably the most aquatic of British newts and usually inhabit the shallow or gently shelving, muddy areas of pools where there is a good growth of submerged, emergent but not floating vegetation. Where stands of pondweed *Potamogeton* species, flote grass, yellow water lily, water violet, hornwort, starwort and arrowhead or, in montane situations, water lobelia, milfoil, rush and spike-rush are present, these are especially favoured.

Palmate newt breeding ponds may be typified as being permanent, shaded, clearwater bodies, over 80 cm in depth with little pollution or disturbance, close to tree cover.

The crested newt is usually found in ponds in company with the smooth newt. The crested is fairly aquatic and occurs in both still and gently flowing waters, reservoirs and ditches though not in small garden ponds. Although said to prefer weedy pools it can often be found in bare quarry ponds and coal washing pools and on the continent of Europe breeds in weedless pools choked with terrestrial plant debris. In some bare pools a growth of the filamentous alga called blanket weed favours the breeding of this species and it is far more tolerant of rather open pools than the other British newts.

Breeding pools are usually clear with a depth of over 30 cm, since crested newt larvae prefer deep water, and are often situated on clay or chalk soils. However, there are also some good duneland colonies in South Wales and north-west England. Often thought of as a lowland species, it occurs to an altitude of 380 metres in the Peak District and 2000 metres in southern Europe. Like the smooth newt it prefers more base-rich (high pH) situations, perhaps with a tendency to colonise even more alkaline pools than the smooth, especially where these are rich in chemical nutrients (hard water). In Norway, however, populations have been recorded from acidic *Sphagnum* bog pools with pH 4.8.

Crested newts are often associated with woodlands but this is not strictly the case. In Essex they avoid woodland, preferring ponds or dykes in rough pasture where flote-grass is abundant, and in Epping Forest they inhabit grassy waters, ornamental ponds and even an old swimming pool. One colony in South Wales inhabits a pool in a city park surrounded by close mown grass, tennis courts and negligible cover. A scientific survey of the crested newt in Britain revealed its optimum habitat to be farm ponds surrounded by a peripheral layer of trees and scrub which did not shade the water excessively and which were adjacent to more extensive woodland. Such pools were mature, nutrient rich, of medium size, able to dessiccate every few years, well vegetated, but with sufficient clear areas to allow the males to display. Crested newts usually share their pools with other newts but normally not with frogs, toads or fish. Mature nutrient-rich pools contain plenty of food items and water plants which themselves provide food for invertebrates, shelter and an egg-laying substrate. Larger ponds provide more food for a large newt but very large ponds may contain predatory fish and are therefore avoided. Ponds which dry out every few years will not sustain a fish population and crested newt larvae seem particularly susceptible to fish predation.

Crested newts require a diverse, densely packed terrestrial habitat (scrub) for shelter and food when on land, and use corridors of suitable habitat, for example, hedges and ditches, to disperse from the breeding pond. Town gardens are good terrestrial habitat but are under-used because of a lack of suitable breeding sites. On land, adult crested newts may also frequent unlikely habitats such as fields of mature wheat.

An ideal crested newt pond has no fish, little pollution, a depth of 50 to 100 cm, a surface area of more than 100 square metres, moderate growth of aquatic vegetation (including submerged terrestrial plants, duckweed and algae and especially starwort) and is surrounded by a mixture of pasture, woodland and scrub but not pure dense woodland, arable fields or pasture.

Within the pond newts show a preference for discrete habitat types. At a site in mid Wales more smooth and palmate newts were encountered in open water than in adjacent reed swamp or at the pond margin. Those found within the swamp were mostly at the surface whilst those collected in the open water occurred at the bottom. More palmates than smooths were observed close to the bank, perhaps indicating a slight difference in habitat selection.

What factors influence a newt's choice of terrestrial habitat? Laboratory studies show that both smooth and crested newts choose moist environments regardless of illumination but, when provided with moist conditions, the smooth newt is photopositive (attracted to light) and the crested newt photonegative during the daytime. At night both are photopositive. This ties in with the less nocturnal nature of the smooth newt.

On land newts seek out moist refuges, stones, logs, corrugated iron sheets, compost and rubbish heaps. On damp nights they move away from these refuges to forage and may even return to their breeding pond outside the normal season. Smooth newts tend to range no further than nine metres from their 'home-stone' and may return to the same area in successive seasons. Crested newts may move more than 200 metres from their breeding pond with juveniles dispersing further, perhaps to avoid predation by their parents. They may travel at a rate of 70 metres per week. A 2 hectare (5 acre) site has been shown to support a population of about two thousand adult crested newts.

WHERE DO NEWTS GO
IN THE WINTER?

Comparatively little is known about newt hibernation or, more correctly, torpidity, because of the obvious difficulties of finding animals during the winter. Traditionally it has been said that newts spend the winter under the soil out of the reach of frost, but crested and smooth newts have been found hibernating in tree stumps, under bark and logs and in piles of leaves. Smooth newts have also been recorded from seaweed-covered walls adjacent to the seashore as well as cellars and mineshafts. One survey of hibernacula also recorded smooth newts inside disused rabbit burrows. Research in Britain has shown that newts hibernating under stones at the beginning of the winter descend further into the soil as temperatures decrease and they have been found to a depth of 10 cm in humus.

What are the essential features of a hibernaculum? All the situations mentioned are damp though not wet and contain a good supply of invertebrate prey. All are frost-free and relatively warm because of the decomposition of plant material. It is not uncommon to find several newts hibernating in close physical contact and aggregations of over a hundred individuals have been unearthed.

Newts may hibernate underwater in their breeding pools, especially the non-metamorphosed larvae, juveniles and

8. *Male smooth newt displaying to a female. The male moves to the front end of the female before waving, whipping and fanning his tail.*

9. *Male crested newt depositing a sperm package in front of the female.*

10. *Larva of the crested newt, a voracious carnivore but very susceptible to fish predation.*

11. *Newts will sometimes tackle very large food items like this earthworm being eaten by a male smooth newt. Occasionally large morsels become jammed in the gullet and the newt drowns.*

12. (Lower left). *A neotenous smooth newt. The light coloration suggests damage to the pituitary gland.*

13. (Lower right). *Crested newt showing belly pattern. The belly coloration may serve as a warning to predators that the animal has a poisonous skin. Belly patterns may be used by scientists to distinguish individual newts.*

young adults which have migrated to the pond in the autumn and are about to breed for the first time. In a semi-captive colony 50 per cent of adult crested and palmate newts returned to the water but no smooth newts were observed to hibernate in the pond. Overwintering by juveniles may occur in ponds that are very shaded or deep, where temperatures are insufficient to promote rapid growth and development. It is likely that overwintering by adult newts occurs only in relatively large water bodies with dense vegetation, where the animals are buffered against severe temperature changes and freezing and where they can remain quite active all winter. There are old records of newts which survived being frozen but these have not been verified.

Frogs and toads likewise choose a wide range of hibernacula.

Newts become less visible during October and November though work in mid Wales revealed much movement between land and water throughout the winter, with the exception of periods of hard weather, and juveniles have been seen emerging from ponds in December. Newts are extremely tolerant of low temperatures and remain active down to temperatures of 0 C (32 F). The end of hibernation is signalled by the commencement of the major migration to the breeding pond in late February or the beginning of March.

Why do newts, as well as frogs and toads, hibernate? Being cold-blooded or ectothermic they cannot maintain their body temperatures much above the temperature of their surroundings. As the air temperature falls so does their body temperature and metabolic processes slow down. They are, therefore, obliged to seek shelter from the worst of the weather, not just to protect themselves from freezing but also from the greater risk of predation and to avoid the problems of food shortage. There also appears to be some relationship between maturation of sexual organs and hibernation. Newts prevented from hibernating do not come into breeding condition.

During hot dry spells newts may aestivate (summer hibernation) on land, hiding away in damp localities and not feeding until conditions ameliorate.

Matrimonials and egg laying

Newts leave their terrestrial haunts to breed and migrate to a pond, as do frogs and toads. Since adults rarely move far from the breeding pond, such migrations are not as spectacular as those exhibited by other amphibians. Migration begins in February or March (occasionally earlier), usually in late afternoon or evening, when temperatures creep above 0 C (32 F) and preferably after rainfall. There is evidence of an autumn migration, especially of sub-adults, and display and egg-laying may occur before winter. Migrating newts tend to move downhill. Males reach the ponds before females and stay there for about a hundred days in the case of smooths and palmates. Males need to arrive first to feed well and develop their crests and toe webs.

Entry into the pond is marked in both sexes by a change in colour, the skin becoming paler and brighter, and males develop their nuptial finery. The dry velvety skin becomes thinner and more absorbent and smooth and the mucous glands begin to secrete. These changes and the urge to return to water are probably influenced by the pituitary hormone prolactin.

Once in the pond females move around more than males and, where there is a current, both sexes tend to move upstream. Adult newts are fairly faithful to breeding ponds and usually return if removed. Newts, especially cresteds, may leave the pond and return several times during the breeding season, particularly if the pond is drying out.

The sex ratio of newts is often biased in favour of females, though in common frogs and toads the reverse is frequently true. Several workers have reported ratios of two or three females to every one male in smooth and palmate newts.

Unlike frogs and toads, newts exhibit complex courtship displays which are performed under water on the bottom of the pond. In the smooth newt courtship begins with the male approaching the female to nudge her cloacal region. She

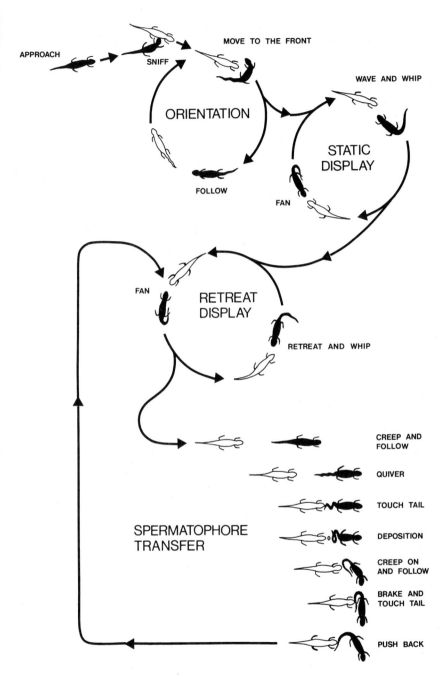

APPROACH

SNIFF

MOVE TO THE FRONT

ORIENTATION

FOLLOW

WAVE AND WHIP

STATIC DISPLAY

FAN

RETREAT DISPLAY

FAN

RETREAT AND WHIP

CREEP AND FOLLOW

QUIVER

TOUCH TAIL

DEPOSITION

CREEP ON AND FOLLOW

BRAKE AND TOUCH TAIL

PUSH BACK

SPERMATOPHORE TRANSFER

14. *The sexual behaviour sequence of the smooth newt; the male is shaded black.*

may move away but her suitor will pursue her, gaining her attention by positioning himself in front of her head. The female finally succumbs to his attentions and becomes less active. The male display, then, has three elements: the wave, whip and fan, performed in no particular order. During fanning the male curves his tail against the side of his body nearest the female and vibrates the end gently but rapidly whilst opening his cloaca. The water currents carry male secretions (from the enlarged dorsal gland which opens into the cloaca) to the female's nose. During the wave the tail is held at an obtuse angle, blocking the female's path and providing a view of his crest and colourful flanks. The whip, which usually follows the wave, is a violent lashing of the tail against the flank, often pushing the male backwards.

The female eventually starts to approach the male and he backs off, whipping and waving until he turns away and creeps 10 cm from the female. There he stops, quivering his tail, waiting for her to catch up and touch his tail with her snout. He then folds and lifts his tail and deposits a spermatophore, a package of sperm enclosed in jelly and resembling an inverted cone. Male newts have no penis hence fertilisation is external and the extruded spermatophore must be accepted and picked up by the female. To ensure acceptance the male moves off to a distance corresponding to his own body length, orientating himself at right angles to the female, blocking her path with his tail. The female approaches to touch his tail and stops with her cloaca above the spermatophore. Should her extended cloaca touch the spermatophore, sperm transfer occurs. The male then pushes the female back with his tail such that she repeats her approach, so ensuring fertilisation. Sometimes spermatophores are deposited earlier in this sequence but they are unlikely to be accepted.

After the sequence the male may back away and begin displaying again, even if the sperm transfer was successful, and the sequence may be repeated several times. The greater the number of sequences the greater the chance of successful fertilisation. It has been estimated that 43 per cent of sexual sequences result in sperma-

tophore transfer. Sometimes the sequence does not result in spermatophore production and occasionally males display to inanimate objects or fish.

The pattern and length of display is largely determined by the behaviour of the female who may advance or retreat at inappropriate moments. Early displays in a series tend to be briefer than later ones, spermatophore deposition occurring quickly after one tail-touch by the female. After several sequences two or three tail-touches may be required. This is probably related to the male's ability to produce spermatophores — the longer the series the fewer spermatophores the male has available to deposit. Over a period of weeks the ability of the male to produce spermatophores will decrease, reflected by a lower number of display sequences in a given time period. Breathing also interrupts courtship, the male having to gulp air at the surface since vigorous display demands much oxygen. However, since breathing may terminate courtship, the male is able to suppress breathing during spermatophore transfer.

One male may not fertilise all of a single female's eggs (each clutch may be fertilised by a number of males), though females generally remain unresponsive to males for twenty days after insemination. Both sexes probably exhibit some partner selection since both will attempt to mate with genetically fit partners. How do they assess fitness? If a female ensures that a male goes through several display sequences she is also ensuring that he is able to produce several spermatophores and that he can stay submerged for long periods (males that have to surface often would run a higher risk of predation and are thus less fit). Crest size may indicate fitness since that is determined by the food-seeking abilities of the male and reflects his ability to absorb dissolved oxygen (over a large surface area). Older, bigger males have larger testes and produce more spermatophores, so females may select by size. Males may select females that show persistence in courtship by increasing the length of each sequence and requiring more tail-touches to induce spermatophore production, bearing in mind that it is usually later sequences that result in insemination.

15. (Left). *The larva of the great diving beetle is a predator of newt larvae.*

16. (Right). *Newly emerged smooth newts. Their colour is similar to that of the adult during the terrestrial phase of its life.*

Males also show a preference for larger, and presumably more fecund, females.

Since smooth and palmate newts often occur in the same ponds some form of reproductive isolation must occur to prevent hybridisation. Females may identify males by their smell, appearance and display. The palmate display, whilst similar to that of the smooth newt, differs in having a subdued wave and less violent whip involving only the end of the tail, and in fanning twice as rapidly but for four times as long as the smooth. Fanning is more common in the palmate and occurs regularly during the male's retreat.

Male smooth and palmate newts have some webbing on the hind feet. These stabilise the body during feeding and when parachuting from the water surface and, also during courtship, prevent the males from swimming backwards whilst whipping and fanning. They may serve as brakes during pursuit movements and give the male more thrust as he heads off his intended mate. The males of both species also have a dorso-lateral ridge, though it is ill-defined in the smooth newt. It forms a groove along the flank which, during fanning, carries water currents to the female's snout. In palmates the groove is deeper to counteract the turbulence caused by more rapid fanning, the tail filament serving a similar function.

Display in the crested newt is essentially similar, though the male may scent-mark to attract a female. During display the male's posture is distinctive as he lifts his hindquarters off the substrate, balancing on his forelimbs, his tail kinked in the middle and angled towards the female. He beats his tail slowly back and forth flicking the tip close to the female, waving his body and crest. He gradually leans towards the female until the tail strikes her head, when he creeps off to produce the spermatophore, often without the encouragement of a tail-touch.

Despite various mechanisms to prevent hybridisation, every type of cross has been obtained under laboratory conditions though possibly only one natural hybrid (between a smooth and a palmate) has ever been found in Britain.

During newt display the pair may be interrupted by other newts, usually males, and some may sneak in to steal the female. This occurs most frequently when the majority of females have laid their eggs and thus available females are limited. Males may also display to males, behaviour which may serve a territorial function as the same males do seem to frequent regular beats. Females occasionally perform pseudo-male behaviour, exhibiting some of the display movements. The reasons for this are not understood.

Newts become sexually mature at the age of four or five years, but in recently colonised ponds maturity seems to be reached sooner, perhaps in two or three years. Larger, older newts lay more and larger eggs, conferring a distinct survival advantage. Over four hundred may be produced with perhaps as many as seven hundred in the smooth newt. Several eggs are laid per day, usually when the water temperature exceeds 9 C (48 F). If conditions are unfavourable the female may not lay all her eggs but retain and resorb them.

The sticky oval newt eggs are laid singly, carefully wrapped in the leaves of aquatic plants by the hind feet of the female, thus hiding them from predators. This is in contrast to the egg masses containing thousands of eggs laid by frogs and toads. Occasionally eggs are laid on blanket weed, debris or on the bottom of ponds, and very rarely in strings. Certain plants are preferred as a laying substrate. Starwort is preferred by all species, whilst crowfoot, water mint, water forget-me-not, water speedwell, water soldier and submerged grass are all favoured. Water violet, *Fontinalis*, water milfoil, Canadian pondweed and *Egeria densa* may be used by the smaller newts.

Hatching occurs after two or three weeks but, like all development phases, this period is dependent on temperature. Thus, newt embryos raised at 25 C (77 F) develop six times faster than those raised at 10 C (50 F). Under normal circumstances the period from hatching to metamorphosis lasts three months though crested newts may develop more quickly.

To break free from its jelly capsule the larva partly digests it, finally releasing itself by vigorous movements. It then moves haphazardly, since it has no limbs, only stalk-like adhesive organs to help attach itself to submerged objects. These organs are absorbed after a few days as the forelimbs grow. For the first few days the larva probably does not feed. The larva possesses external gills which become more branched as it grows and contain a complex of blood vessels to allow absorption of oxygen directly from the water. Oxygen is also absorbed by blood vessels in the tail and skin. Hind limbs appear after six weeks. In frogs and toads it is the hind limbs which appear first. Upon metamorphosis the gills and tail fin are lost and breathing is achieved predominantly by the lungs, though respiration across the skin still occurs, allowing the newt to stay submerged for considerable periods. The sound of newts gulping for air at the surface of a pond with a characteristic 'plop' is familiar to all newt watchers. Air is forced to the lungs using the throat, which pumps constantly when newts are on land.

An odd situation prevails in crested newts, where 50 per cent mortality of embryos has been observed to occur in the late 'tail bud' stage of egg development. This 'programmed death' is apparently built into the genes of the species but its function remains a mystery.

Another strange developmental phenomenon is neoteny, in which various juvenile characters (external gills, tail fin, juvenile coloration) are retained for longer periods than normal, a condition which can be observed in the familiar laboratory salamander, the axolotl *Ambystoma mexicanum*. This may occur where metamorphosis has been delayed by environmental factors and will continue even when favourable conditions arise. In this case the animals are unable to reproduce (partial neoteny) though occasionally newts have been observed to produce spawn whilst juvenile characteristics, for example gills, are retained, these being lost at some later stage. Partial neoteny occurs most frequently in deep or cold water-bodies; where a barrier to emergence exists; or in water with high organic content.

Under certain conditions, the neotenic state can become permanent, the animals being unable to metamorphose or breed (probably because the males are unable to produce sperm). This occurs where there has been damage to the thyroid gland, which promotes metamorphosis, or the pituitary; neotenous newts often show signs of albinism, a state also linked with pituitary damage. Neotenous individuals rise infrequently to the pond surface, absorbing oxygen via the skin and gills. Neoteny may occur in all three British newts but is rarely recorded in the palmate.

Food

Amphibians operate rather like pitfall traps, snapping up any living creature encountered that is not too large or ferocious. Occasionally their judgement fails them and it is not infrequent to find newts that have choked and drowned with large food items wedged in the gullet.

When feeding under water, adult newts and larvae snap up food with the jaws but on land smooth and palmate newts, but rarely crested, often catch small prey by flicking out their short tongues. Use of the tongue underwater is rarely recorded. Once in the mouth prey are prevented from escaping by a double row of tiny teeth on either side of the palate and jaws, which are replaced in sequence throughout the newt's life.

It has been suggested that one of the reasons why male smooth and palmate newts have webbed hind feet may be to assist in feeding. The males, being lighter than females, require webs to stabilise their bodies during the vigorous feeding movements.

In water, newts will eat water-lice (*Asellus sp.*), shrimps (*Gammarus sp.*) and other small crustaceans such as *Daphnia* as well as worms, insect larvae and their aquatic adults, terrestrial invertebrates stranded on the water surface, single-celled protozoans and even water snails. Favourite prey items are tadpoles, though only the crested newt regularly eats toad tadpoles, presumably because of their distasteful skin secretions. It has been estimated that a dozen

17. *Water starwort, one of the aquatic plants most favoured by newts for egg-laying.*

crested newts could, in one breeding season, eat every tadpole produced by one clump of frog spawn. Smooth newts and probably the other species will eat the spawn itself, extracting the black centres and leaving the jelly behind. Female newts have even been observed laying eggs and promptly eating them, and newt larvae are probably fairly common dietary items. Crested newts will quite readily eat smaller newts, including adult smooths.

Whether newts exercise any selection in obtaining food is debatable but small newts eat smaller prey than large newts, and smooth newts kill smaller tadpoles than crested newts. Experimental evidence suggests that smooth newts select larger *Daphnia* when given the choice of large and small species, but that this selection could be overridden by presenting smaller but darker (more visible) *Daphnia*. In different ponds newts seem to exhibit different preferences, such that in one study 75 per cent of the adult smooth newt's diet (and 40 per cent of the diet of smooth newt larvae) comprised *Daphnia*. At a second site palmates fed mostly on fly larvae and cr025eds on *Asellus* and snails. However, at a Welsh pond smooths and palmates showed no selection in terms of species, taking prey items in proportion to availability but selecting only small *Asellus* and *Gammarus*.

Newts are carnivorous but also ingest some plant material. At one pool 14 per cent of smooths and 25 per cent of palmates contained vegetable material and detritus which may have been swallowed intentionally, by accident or have originated from the guts of their prey. Recently hatched newts undoubtedly feed on large amounts of microscopic plant matter (phytoplankton) and may subsist upon it exclusively.

On land newts have equally catholic diets and the usual selection of slow-moving invertebrates is taken, mostly at twilight. Crested newts have been known to eat baby slow-worms. Newts (which possess colour vision) are attracted by movement, and the sight of live prey can drive them into a frenzy. They snap up anything in the vicinity, including plants and the extremities of other newts, often inflicting considerable damage. They also use their sense of smell, particularly underwater, and can be attracted by non-living food items such as pieces of meat, fish or fish food. Laboratory tests have shown that crested newts caught tadpoles once in every eight attempts, presumably locating prey at a distance by sight, stalking it and lunging from a distance of 2 cm. A blind crested newt proved even more adept at catching tadpoles, perhaps locating them by smell and by their movements and lunging when much closer.

Threats and mortality

DEFENCE

During the terrestrial phase the dorsal surface of the newt becomes a dark subdued colour, occasionally mottled with darker spots, suggesting that the newt's first line of defence is camouflage. Large larvae and newly metamorphosed smooth newts are photonegative in the daytime, that is they hide from the light, an obvious adaptation to escape predation. Oddly, aquatic larvae are photopositive, perhaps an adaptation to seeking food in the sunniest parts of the pond. To improve camouflage newt skin contains pigment cells or chromatophores which change the animal's colour depending upon background colour, light intensity, surface texture, temperature and humidity.

In addition all British newts have skins capable of secreting poisonous substances (alkaloids similar to digitalis), although in the smaller species this does not appear to deter most predators. The crested newt has a larger number of skin glands along the back and tail, some of which produce a thick whitish secretion which irritates the mucous membranes of mammals, reptiles and other newts. These secretions are said to smell of horseradish. To humans the poison is harmless, unless the newt is placed inside the mouth, but may irritate cuts in the skin. A chewed newt will cause salivation,

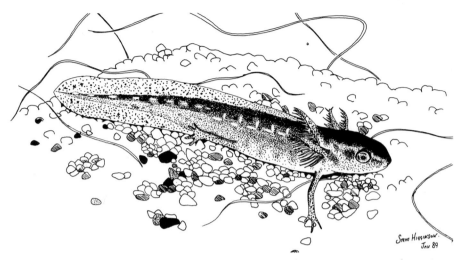

18. *Palmate newt larva. The larva of the smooth newt is almost indistinguishable.*

convulsions and headache. The deterrent effect of these secretions has been observed on cats, terrapins and grass snakes.

The bright yellow belly colour of the crested newt may serve as a warning, warding off predators such as fish approaching from below. There is evidence that the closely related alpine crested newt uses its belly coloration in defensive postures on land. When threatened, it rolls up its tail, turns its head to one side and closes its eyes, revealing the yellow base to its tail. Further attacks result in more belly coloration being revealed before the newt attempts to bite its attacker.

Two other means of defence are open to the newt: rapid flight away from the predator by lashing its tail, holding its limbs against the body (for streamlining) and swimming for the cover of waterweed; and uttering a squeak when lifted from the water, a habit which never fails to surprise.

Newts have no tympanum (ear-drum) and so their hearing on land is probably poor, unlike that of most frogs and toads, though they can pick up the vibrations of approaching predators. In water, rows of sensory pores on the head, flanks and tail detect movement in the same way as does the lateral line of fish.

PREDATORS AND PARASITES

Newts are preyed upon by a whole range of aquatic and terrestrial predators. Despite this there are records of life-spans of 27 years for a female crested newt and 20 years for smooth and palmate newts (sexes unspecified), though these figures refer to captive specimens. Newt larvae are eaten by carnivorous invertebrates, including the great pond snail (*Lymnaea stagnalis*), whilst the caddis larva (*Limnephilus vittatus*) is a major predator of smooth newt larvae. Hydra also kill larvae but may be too small to eat them. Large water beetles such as *Dytiscus marginalis* are even capable of attacking adults of the smaller newts and the large blood-sucking leeches *Hirudo medicinalis* and *Hemiclepsis marginata* may cause severe debilitation.

Sticklebacks are notorious predators of larvae and few fish are averse to adding them to their diet, though large populations of newts are known from some ponds containing carp and goldfish. Curiously, the larvae of crested newts seem less able to withstand fish predation, perhaps because they lack the cryptic coloration of the other species and have a tendency to swim in mid water rather than rest on the bottom. They are rarely present in fish-ponds. Newt larvae fall prey to waterbirds such as moorhens,

21

ducks, gulls, rails and herons and probably also to opportunistic feeders like wagtails and members of the thrush family. Herons, gulls and crows will also take adult newts. Predatory mammals such as the water shrew will eat newly metamorphosed amphibians as will carabid beetles, hedgehogs, mustelids (weasel family), foxes, rats, mice and cats. Even grazing mammals pose a threat when eating grasses and weeds in shallow pools. The grass snake is a major amphibian predator. On land the crested newt probably suffers less predation because of its poisonous skin.

More insidious are the various parasitic and disease organisms which infest newts. Most newts and their larvae carry parasites though these rarely cause totally debilitating effects. In one pond 81 per cent of newts carried a thorny-headed worm (*Acanthocephalus anthuris*), whilst other newts carry a variety of roundworms, horsehair worms and occasionally a tapeworm (*Diphyllobothrium latum*), which completes its development in humans. Trematodes (parasitic flatworms) may occur in the gut, mouth, bladder, and muscles or as cysts or pigment patches on the skin. Cysts may also be caused by protozoans which likewise infest the gut and bladder. One species, *Oodinium pillularis*, appears as a grey deposit over the skin, with lethal results. Some parasites occur in the blood and are transmitted via leeches as the intermediate host. Various fungi, for example *Saprolegnia*, attack damaged or sick newts and their eggs, but perhaps the most unusual of parasites are the larvae (or glochidia) of freshwater mussels (*Anodonta* and *Unio*) which attach themselves to the skin of the newt and remain encysted there for several weeks.

Bacterial and viral infections are less well known and represent a challenge to the enterprising veterinarian. Dermal ulcers caused by bacterial or actinomycete (yeast) agents cause devastating deterioration of the skin and bone in captive newts, eventually killing them. 'Molchpest' is another highly contagious syndrome causing sluggishness, anorexia, oedema, reddening and abcessing of the skin and uncoordinated movement. The cause is unknown but it is almost always lethal. Skin tumours, occasionally seen on British newts, may also have a viral origin.

With odds stacked against them it is not surprising that newts suffer heavy mortality in certain stages of the life cycle. On average only one in eleven smooth newt tadpoles survive to metamorphosis, one in five newtlets survive each year until maturity and one in two adults survive in each subsequent year. Females apparently do better than males, which in the aquatic phase suffer a 10 per cent higher mortality than females. Similar mortality rates have been obtained for other species, including the crested, where more might be expected to survive because of their toxic skin.

CHANGING COATS AND LOSING LIMBS

Newts have very sensitive skins with groups of sense organs around the head and along the back and tail. Like the lateral line of a fish these enable the newt to maintain equilibrium and posture whilst providing information about what is happening in the surrounding water. When newts leave water the skin thickens and the sensory cells are reduced.

Newts, like other amphibians, regularly shed the outer layers of the skin (ecdysis), a process which is under the control of the pituitary gland situated adjacent to the brain and which occurs in response to food, environmental conditions, disease and growth. Diseased newts shed their skins frequently, sometimes every day. Shedding begins with the skin at the front of the head splitting and the old skin slipping backwards like a stocking. The newt may rub against other objects to loosen the skin further. It is eventually pushed off at the end of the tail with the snout and usually eaten. Newts entering the pond in spring usually eat their shed skins as the first meal of the season.

More spectacular is the ability to regenerate lost limbs. Young newts are better able to regenerate them than older ones and regeneration is more successful at the front end of the body; a crested newt can regenerate a forelimb in under six months. Newts are also able to regenerate parts of the tail and the eye, including the entire lens and associated nerves. Statements in old texts suggesting that they can regenerate a lost head do, however, seem a little far-fetched.

Conservation and study

By the early 1960s naturalists had observed a decline in all newt species. Urbanisation, drainage, water abstraction, afforestation, rubbish dumping, pollution, agricultural change, mining and even the popularity of the cat and goldfish were cited as causal factors, whilst more recently acidification, wilful killing, collection, motor vehicles and the development of trout fisheries have had a significant adverse effect. Declines in the crested newt in northern and western Britain were particularly worrying and in 1973 the Conservation Committee of the British Herpetological Society published a policy for the protection of native herpetofauna. Between 1966 and 1974, crested newt sites declined by 50 per cent and from 1980 to 1985 a further 2 per cent loss of sites was estimated, though many more were damaged. Since this species rarely utilises small ponds the vogue for garden ponds has not counterbalanced the loss of pools in the wider countryside. Significant declines in crested newt populations have been noted from their strongholds in the Midlands and East Anglia. On a positive note, both smooth and palmate newts are declining less now than in the 1960s, though all three species have continued to decline in continental Europe.

As a result, all British Newts received protection under Schedule 5 of the Wildlife and Countryside Act 1981, rendering commercial exploitation and destruction illegal. The crested newt received full protection such that it is illegal to catch, possess or handle the species except under licence. The Act also forbids the introduction of foreign species which may compete with native animals. Britain is a signatory to the Bern Convention which further strengthens species protection

and provides a framework for habitat protection. Several nature reserves are now managed for the crested newt. Like all British newts, the crested will increase rapidly under semi-captive conditions and a bank of captive bred animals has been established for use in reintroduction projects.

Action to protect sites has often been taken late, resulting in compromises which damage the aquatic and terrestrial habitats or result in translocation or habitat creation schemes of questionable value, particularly where sites are chosen not upon scientific criteria but simply upon appearance. There is a danger that animals may be translocated to ponds which already have a full complement of newts and therefore are unable to support more, or to ponds which are too new, or whose physical and chemical characteristics render them unsuitable for long-term colonisation. Protection of the breeding pond is insufficient, as good-quality terrestrial habitat is essential, in the case of the crested newt, to a radius of about 200 metres from the pond.

Garden ponds can be successful in supporting populations of the smaller newts and there is a record of all three species breeding in a garden pond of 130 cm by 150 cm by 50 cm deep. Smooth newts will even colonise sunken sinks. Smooth or palmate newts will colonise gardens if the animals occur in the surrounding countryside, and crested newts may become established in large garden pools if translocated during the breeding season. One study centred in Brighton, East Sussex, revealed that 16 per cent of gardens had ponds and of these 15 to 20 per cent contained newts; sadly another study revealed that 24 per cent of garden ponds were subsequently removed in a comparatively short time.

To protect newts research into their requirements is essential, and estimates of populations at breeding sites are particularly necessary. Counting newts during the day is a poor indication of population but, for crested newts, counting at night with the aid of a torch when the animals are active at the surface may account for 10 per cent of the population using the pond. Netting is relatively inefficient and damages weed beds, though it can give an indication of spatial distribution. Better results can be achieved by setting bottle-traps or funnel-traps similar to minnow-traps used by anglers. No bait is necessary but it is essential to check the trap at least every twelve hours (more frequently during warm weather) to prevent captured newts drowning. Traps tied to poles at known depth can give a good idea of spatial distribution and are particularly useful in steep-sided, turbid or weedy ponds, although they work best where newt populations are small. They seem to catch males selectively for reasons that are not clear.

Population estimates can be obtained by trapping the newts as they enter or leave the pool by surrounding the pond with a polythene drift fence buried just below the soil surface and extending above ground to 30 cm. Newts may be captured on both sides of the fence by inserting pitfall traps. Such traps are also useful in gauging home ranges.

Accurate assessment of populations is best achieved by mark-recapture techniques in which a known number of newts are marked and released: none of these procedures should be attempted by the amateur. The population can then be sampled for marked individuals and, by calculation, the number of marked individuals recaptured can be estimated as a proporation of the entire population. Marking is difficult since newt legs cannot be ringed like those of birds. Toe-clipping has been used, but newts will regenerate lost digits. Dye-marking under the skin of the tail with Alcian Blue dye using a high pressure jet allows for a combination of marks in different places to give precise information on date of capture, whilst photographing the belly pattern is an accurate, if tedious, method of identification for long term studies. On the continent of Europe marking has even been achieved by transplanting pieces of belly skin on to the backs of crested newts.

Marking of larvae presents greater problems but some success has been achieved using Neutral Red dye to stain common frog tadpoles.

How might age be assessed? Whilst large newts are generally old animals the reverse does not always follow, though body size in male smooth newts appears to be correlated with age. Size may be partially controlled by genetic and environmental factors. An estimate of age has been obtained, but only using dead newts by sectioning the humerus, whereupon annual growth rings like those of a tree can be counted.

Further reading

Arnold, E. N., and Burton J. A. *A Field Guide to the Reptiles and Amphibians of Europe*. Collins, 1978.

Arnold, H. R. (editor). *Provisional Atlas of the Amphibians and Reptiles of the British Isles*. Biological Records Centre, Monks Wood, Natural Environmental Research Council, 1973.

Cooke, A. S., and Scorgie, H. R. A. *Focus on Nature Conservation Number 3. The Status of the Commoner Amphibians and Reptiles in Britain*. Nature Conservancy Council, 1983.

Frazer, D. *Reptiles and Amphibians in Britain*. Collins, 1983.

Griffiths, R. *How to begin the study of Amphibians*. Richmond Publishing, 1987.

Smith, M. *The British Amphibians and Reptiles*. Collins, fifth edition 1973.

Steward, J. W. *The Tailed Amphibians of Europe*. David and Charles, 1969.

ACKNOWLEDGEMENTS:

Thanks are due to Mark Nicholson and Richard Griffiths for information supplied; to Tim Halliday and Bailliere-Tindall for permission to reproduce figure 14; to Angela Rhodes for typing the manuscript and to Louise Wisniewski, Janet Kear and Arnold Cooke for checking. Illustrations are acknowledged as follows: S. Higginson, 3, 17, 18; Eric and David Hosking, 1; 15, 16 (G. E. Hyde); 4, 6, 12 (W. S. Pitt); Frank Lane Picture Agency, 10 (Sylvestris/Müller), 13 (R. Wilmshurst); Natural Science Photos, cover, 5, 8, 9, 11 (G. Kinns); 7 (C. Mattison), 2 (R. Revels).